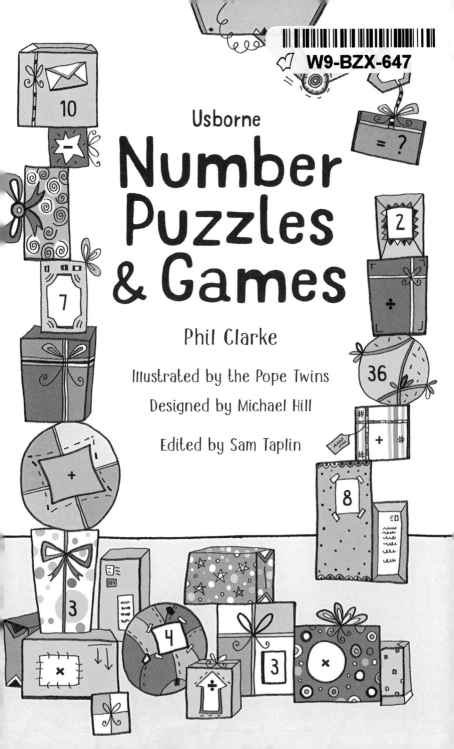

Usborne

Number Puzzles & Games

Phil Clarke

Illustrated by the Pope Twins

Designed by Michael Hill

Edited by Sam Taplin

Pyramid

Fill the blank blocks so that each number
is the sum of the two directly beneath it.

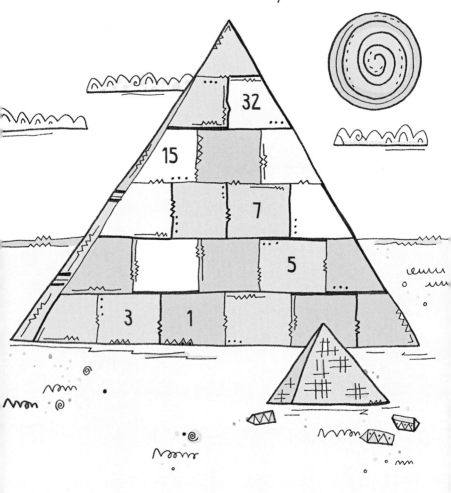

32

15

7

5

3   1

Busy builders

It takes a team of workers two hours to cut out
five blocks from the pyramid-builder's quarry.
How many teams would be needed to produce
500 blocks in an eight-hour working day?

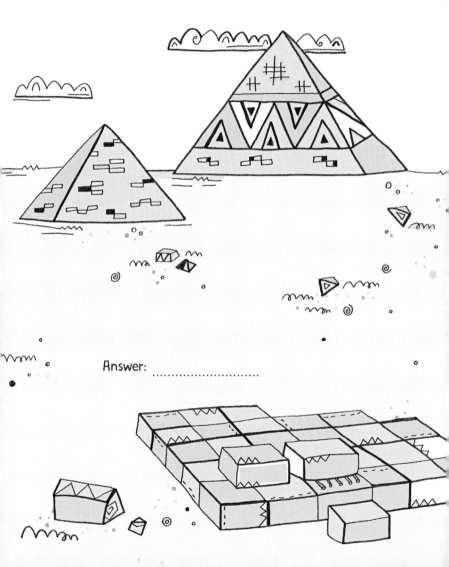

Answer: ....

Shade by numbers

Shade in all the shapes that have a number you can divide by ten to see a hidden sea creature.

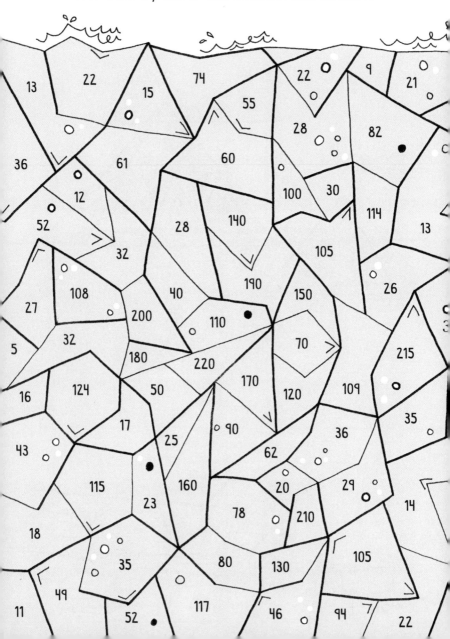

Castle sudoku

The grid below is made up of six sections, each containing six squares. Fill in the blank squares so that each section, row and column contains all the numbers 1 to 6.

5

Fizz-buzz

A counting game for two or more players

In this game, fizz, buzz and fizz-buzz replace certain numbers:

Fizz

Numbers you can divide by 3, such as 3, 6, 9, 12 and so on.

Buzz

Numbers you can divide by 5, such as 5, 10, 20, 25 and so on.

Fizz-buzz

Numbers you can divide by both 3 and 5, such as 15 and 30.

1

Count up from one, taking turns to say a number, or the word that replaces it:

One   Two   Fizz   Four   Buzz

2

See how far you can get. If anyone hesitates, or makes a mistake, they're out.

Eleven   Fizz   Thirteen   Fourteen   Err...

Bulls and cows

A pen-and-paper game for two players

1

Both players secretly write down a three-digit number. All the digits must be different.

287

2

Take turns to guess each other's number, writing your guesses on another piece of paper. Then write next to each other's guesses how many 'bulls' and 'cows' there are.

BULL
a correct digit in the correct place

COW
a correct digit in the wrong place

Example:

Guess 1:	012	C
Guess 2:	345	
Guess 3:	678	CC
Guess 4:	304	
Guess 5:	134	
Guess 6:	234	B
Guess 7:	267	BB
Guess 8:	268	BC
Guess 9:	287	BBB

Two of these digits are correct, but in the wrong place.

3

The first to get three bulls, finding the secret number, is the winner.

Cross-sum

Fit numbers from 1 to 9 into the squares so that each line, across and down, adds up to the total shown in the triangles at each end. You can use numbers more than once, but each number in a line must be different.

Tricky triangles

How many triangles can you count in the pattern below?

Dr. Jafri's journey

Dr. Jafri left home at 7:00am. It took her six minutes to walk through the park. She stopped for two minutes to buy a newspaper. It then took 12 minutes to reach the station. She waited five minutes for her train. Her train journey, normally 18 minutes, was delayed by seven minutes.
The final walk to her surgery took ten minutes.
Draw hands on the clock to show
what time she arrived.

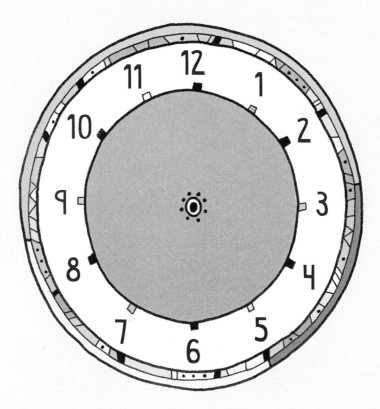

Missing icon

Each of the four different app icons below has a
value between one and nine. Figure out the values
of the icons, and draw in the missing one. The
sum of each line and column is shown.

What's my number?

A game for two or more players

1

One person thinks of a number between 1 and 100.

26

2

The rest take turns to ask questions that can be answered Yes or No to narrow down the possible answers.

Is it bigger than 50?

No

Is it even?

Yes

Does it have a two in it?

Yes

3

The questioners get a total of ten questions between them. Guesses count as questions.

4

If someone guesses right, they win. If no one guesses right, the thinker wins.

Reigning Danes

Study the facts below to find out when each king ruled Denmark, then draw lines to their reigns on the timeline.

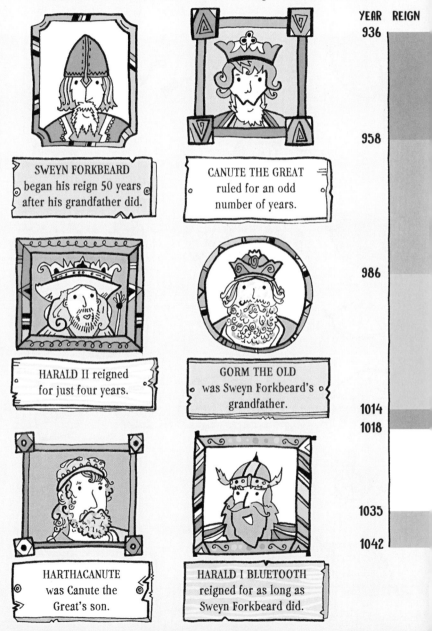

SWEYN FORKBEARD began his reign 50 years after his grandfather did.

CANUTE THE GREAT ruled for an odd number of years.

HARALD II reigned for just four years.

GORM THE OLD was Sweyn Forkbeard's grandfather.

HARTHACANUTE was Canute the Great's son.

HARALD I BLUETOOTH reigned for as long as Sweyn Forkbeard did.

YEAR   REIGN
936
958
986
1014
1018
1035
1042

Calculation trail

Can you complete this super-sized calculation,
doing each part as you reach it?

Start here

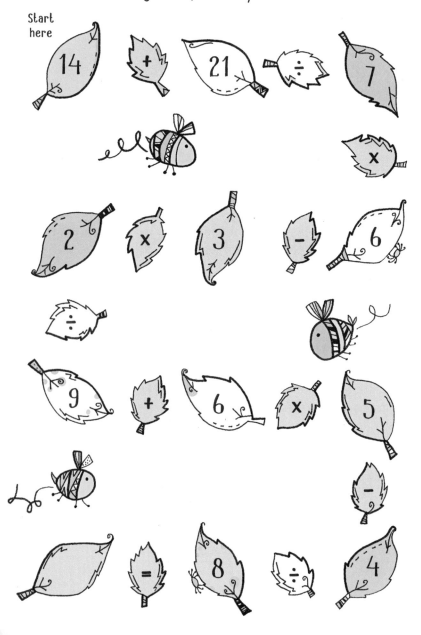

Word sums

In the words below, each letter stands for a
different number between 1 and 6. Can you
find out the value of each letter,
and the final word?

to = 3

root = 10

for = 13

trees = 16

forest =

Turtle trail

Guide Trinny the turtle to the orange sponges for an undersea snack. To reach them, she needs to pass by numbers that add up to exactly 50.

Trinny

8

4

3

5

5

7

2

13

7

6

11

1

8

9

10

Subtle circles

Can you arrange the numbers 1 to 9
in the circles so that the numbers
in each circle add up to 11?

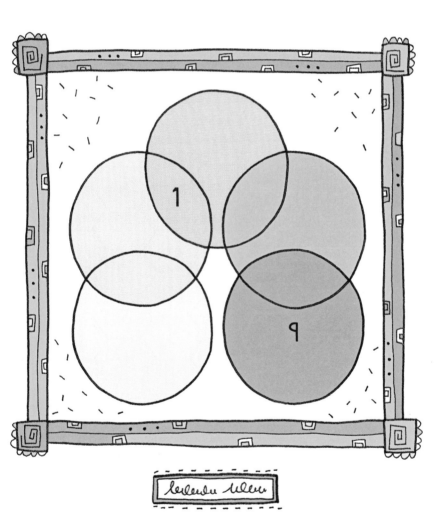

Stepping stones

Intrepid explorer Marco Bravado has to cross these tricky stepping stones to reach the Jewel of Wisdom. Stepping on the wrong stones will set off a deadly booby-trap. The message on the sign is supposed to help him cross safely. Can you mark his route to the Jewel?

If I'm even, halve me. If I'm odd, times three and add one.

Roll the dice

Two dice are rolled together. The table below shows
the 36 possible combinations you could roll. Finish
filling it in, then use it to answer the questions.

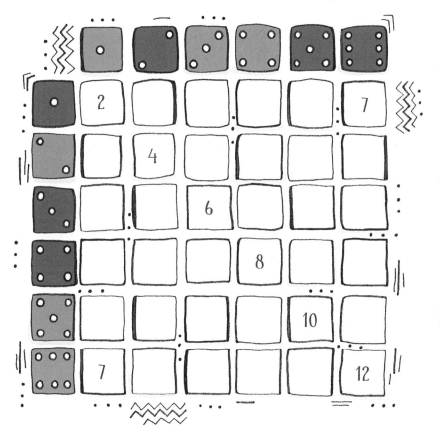

1. Which score are you most likely to roll? ....

2. Which two scores are least likely? ....

3. Which statement is true?

   Rolling the same number twice is...

a. ...LESS likely than rolling a total of six.

b. ...MORE likely than rolling a total of six.

c. ...JUST AS likely as rolling a total of six.   (Circle your answer)

Balancing act

Each jar has its weight on it. Cross out enough jars on the heavier side to balance the scales.

Draw lines to fence off the field into seven areas so that each area has the same number of squares as trees.

Anteater feast

Each anteater needs 20 ants for a satisfying
mid-morning snack. Will any anteater go hungry?

Nathan the naturalist is studying ants. He has made a table of all his observations. Can you help him finish it by writing the correct number in each blank box?

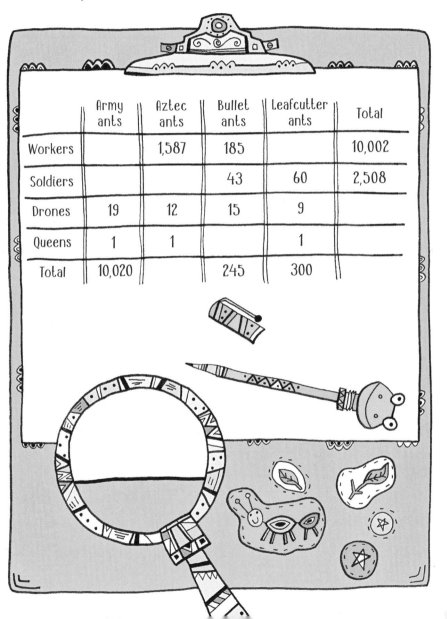

	Army ants	Aztec ants	Bullet ants	Leafcutter ants	Total
Workers		1,587	185		10,002
Soldiers			43	60	2,508
Drones	19	12	15	9	
Queens	1	1		1	
Total	10,020		245	300	

Fifteen

A pen-and-paper game for two players

1

The goal of this game is to pick three numbers that add up to 15.

2

Write out the numbers 1-9 in a grid:

1   2   3

3

Take turns picking a number. One player circles them, the other uses squares. The first with three that make 15 wins. Each number can only be picked once.

4   5   6

7   8   9

4

In this game, the circle player has won.

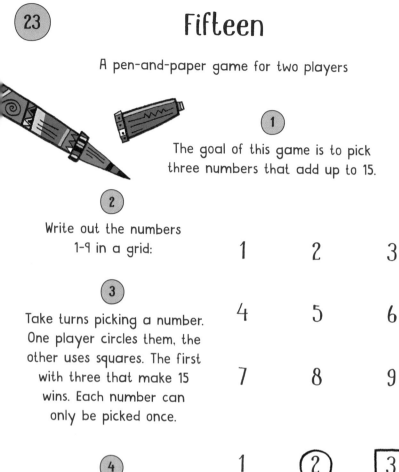

5

Take turns to start, and see who wins the most out of five games.

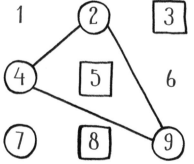

Pizza pattern

Find out how to use the numbers on the outer circles of the top pizza to make the number in the middle using a mixture of adding, subtracting, multiplying or dividing. Then use the same pattern to fill in the gaps on the other pizzas.

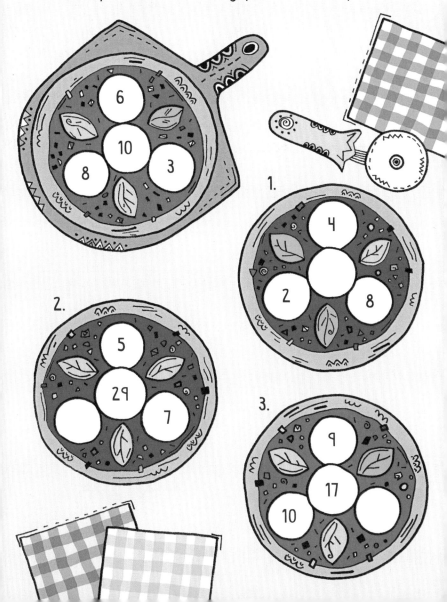

Missing signs

Add the missing sign $+$ $-$ $\times$ or $\div$
to each calculation to make it correct.

Example:

$1 + 2 \quad 3 \quad 4 - 5 = 23 \times$

$1 + 2 \quad 3 + 4 - 5 = 23 \checkmark$

(1 + 234 - 5 does not equal 23, but 1 + 23 + 4 - 5 does.)

1. $1 \quad 2 \times 3 + 4 \quad 5 = 35$

2. $1 \quad 2 \quad 3 \quad 4 - 5 = 41$

3. $1 \quad 2 \times 3 \quad 4 + 5 = 14$

4. $1 + 2 + 3 + 4 \quad 5 = 5$

5. $1 \quad 2 - 3 \quad 4 \quad 5 = 54$

6. $1 \quad 2 \quad 3 \quad 4 \quad 5 = 168$

Dot-to-dot

Starting from 3, join the dots, going up
in 3s, to see a rainforest creature.

Birds on a wire

Find out each number sequence
and add its missing number.

1.

5   8   11   17

2.

  6   12   24   48

3.

7   9   12   14

4.

3   8   6   9

Island bridges

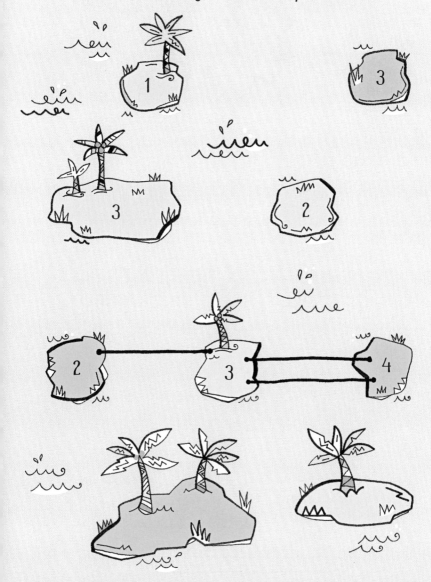

Draw straight lines to build bridges horizontally and vertically between the islands so that each island's number matches the number of bridges coming from it. There can be no more than two bridges between any two islands.

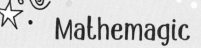

Mathemagic

Wow your friends with these mathematical magic tricks.
Make sure you rehearse them plenty of times.

Mind reader

(1)
Say to your friend:
"Think of a number
from 1–10."

(2)
"Now
double it."

(3)
"Now add
eight."

(4)
"Next, halve your
new number."

(5)
"Now subtract the number
you first thought of."

(6)
"Now turn the result into a
letter: A=1, B=2, and so on."

(7)
"Next, think of a country
beginning with that letter."

(8)
"Finally, think of an
animal beginning
with that country's
second letter."

(9)
Now announce, very
mysteriously, "I sense
that you are thinking of...
an elephant in Denmark!"

(Note: This trick works 99% of the time)

Magic number

1

For this trick, you'll need two pieces of paper and a pen. Or your friend could use a calculator, if you have one.

2

Say you are going to write down a number on your piece of paper, and secretly write 1089.

3

Ask your friend to write down a number with three different digits, for example 152.

4

Next, ask your friend to write the number backwards: 251

5

Now tell your friend to subtract the smaller number from the larger number:
251 - 152 = 99

6

Their answer may have two or three digits. If it has two, tell your friend to put '0' in front: 099

7

Next, ask your friend to write this number backwards: 990

8

Lastly, add the two numbers together:
990 + 099 = 1089

9

Now reveal the number 1089 to your amazed friend!

1089

Magic box

Can you fill in the squares with the missing numbers from 1-8, so that every line of three yellow squares adds up to the number in the middle?

Dot-to-dot

Starting from 4, join the dots, going up in
4s, to see a famous Australian animal.

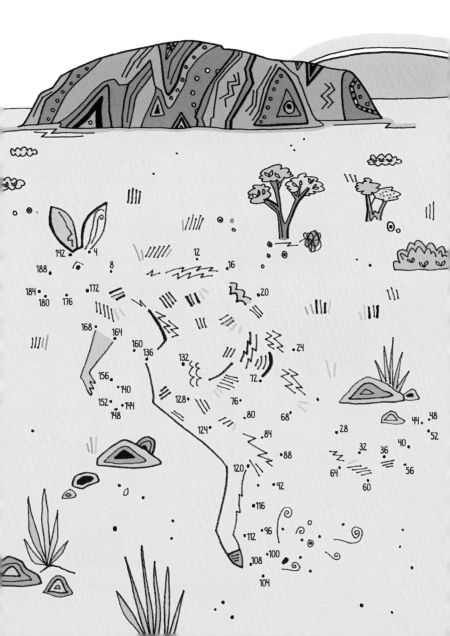

Crossnumber

Solve the clues to fill in the
numbers, across and down.

ACROSS

1. Three hundred and eighty-six thousand,
   seven hundred and twenty-one
4. 307+308+309+310
6. Alice was born in 1994. In which
   year was her 9th birthday?
9. One hundred and thirty-three thousand,
   nine hundred and fifty-six

DOWN

1. 96+107+118
2. (8×80)+(80×80)
3. The sum of the digits of 4 across
5. (4×8×100)+3+7+13
7. Number of days in a leap year
8. 3×7

Pole position

33

Who will be the champion? The table shows the drivers and their final positions in each race. Use the score chart to finish filling in the points, then write the correct names on the gold, silver and bronze trophies.

Position	1st	2nd	3rd	4th	5th
Points	30	20	15	10	5

Race	Steve FLEET	Max SCHNELL	Vera VITESSE	Grigori TACHYON	Festas LAITINEN
1	1st	2nd	4th 10	5th	3rd
2	5th	1st	2nd 20	3rd	5th
3	4th	2nd	5th 5	3rd	1st
4	3rd	3rd	1st 30	2nd	4th
5	1st	2nd	3rd 15	4th	5th
6	2nd	4th	5th 5	3rd	1st
			85		

Beetle

A pencil-and-paper game for two or more players

1

Everyone needs some paper and a pencil. The goal is to be first to finish drawing a beetle with the parts shown below.

2

To draw each part you need the right score. You can roll dice if you have them, or take turns to shut your eyes and pick a number with a pencil from the next page.

3

You need a six to start, by drawing the body. You also need the head before you can add any eyes or feelers.

4

The first to draw all the parts shouts "Beetle!" and wins the game.

6 - Body   5 - Head   4 - Wing   3 - Eye   2 - Feeler   1 - Leg

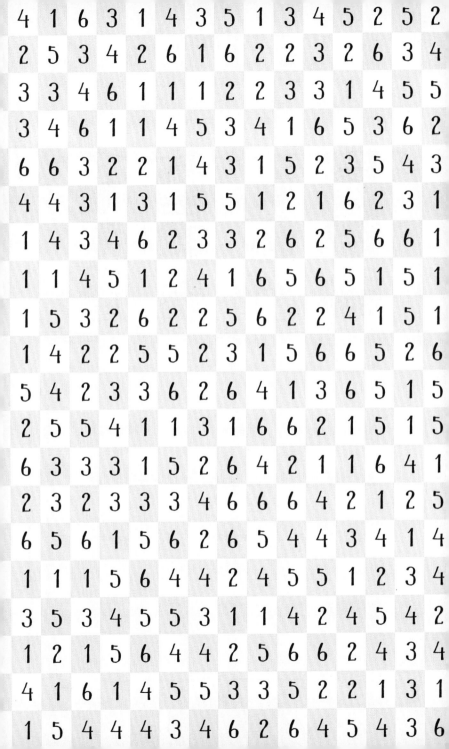

Maya mathematics

The Maya people of Central America used dot and line symbols for numbers. Look at the calculations below and see if you can draw in the missing symbol.

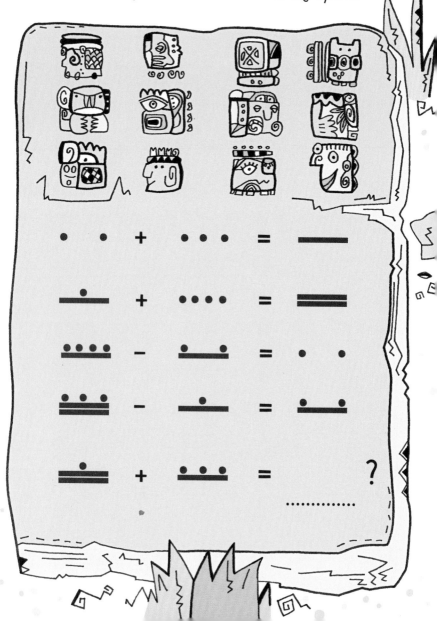

Six sudoku

The grid below is made up of six blocks, each containing six squares. Fill in the blank squares so that each block, row and column contains all the numbers 1 to 6.

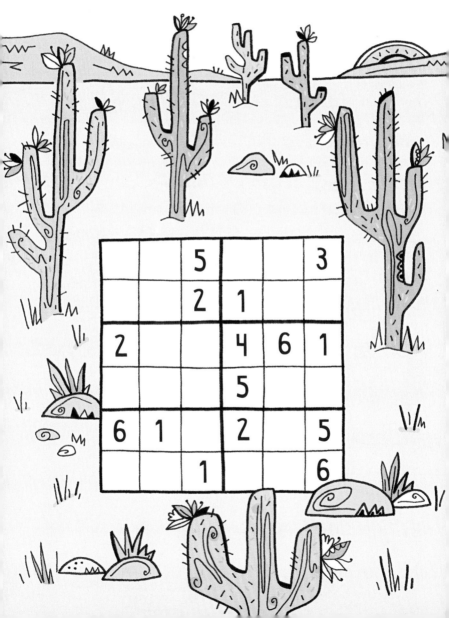

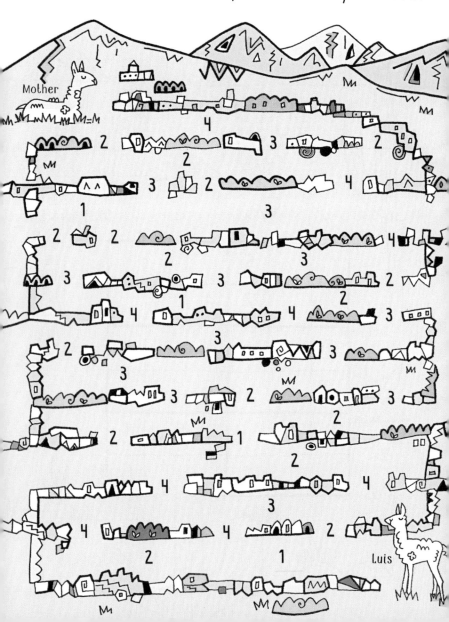

Llama drama

Luis the llama has lost his mother. Help him find his way back up to her through the ancient ruins. The numbers tell you how many seconds each section takes. Can you do it in exactly 30 seconds?

How many hummingbirds?

Are there more hummingbirds with purple cheeks, or with purple throats?

Number-bond tennis

An action game for two players

1

Number bonds are pairs of numbers that add up to round numbers like 10, 20, 50 or 100. For this game, start by using number bonds that add up to 10.

2

Stand facing each other, holding imaginary rackets. Whoever is serving first swings their racket and calls out a number.

3

The other player hits it back while calling out its matching number bond. The first player then serves another number, and so on, back and forth.

4

Then switch around so that the other player is serving. When you've mastered tennis with 10 as a target, move on to 20, 50 and 100.

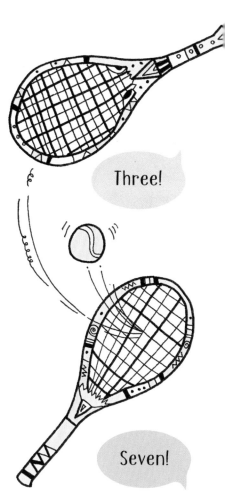

Three!

Seven!

Number criss-cross

Can you fit all the numbers below
into the white squares?

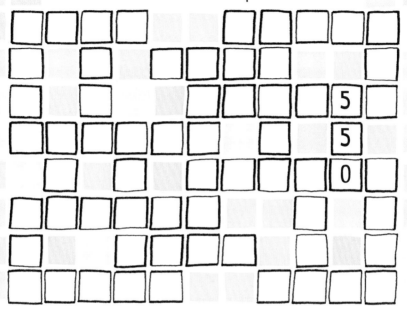

345	3424	8254	128453
376	3649	25035	434709
492	4326	31827	468738
~~550~~	4761	63978	719782
662	5634	79733	727405
883	5979		
	8155		

Circles and squares

Fit all the numbers 1 to 9 in the grid so that the number in each circle is the sum of the four squares around it, and the totals of the orange, green and yellow areas add up to the ones shown at the bottom.

Parrot puzzle

42

The orange parrot eats fruit with numbers that can be divided by two. The yellow parrot eats fruit with numbers that can be divided by three. Which has the most fruit to eat?

Solution search

Solve the calculations, then draw around
the answers hidden in the numbers.

Example:

$30 \div 2 - 3 =$ 1 5 6 12 4 7

1. $7 \times 5 - 24 + 6 =$ 1 7 4 5 9 2 8

2. $18 \div 3 \times 5 - 2 =$ 4 5 0 2 8 1 3

3. $9 \times 8 \div 6 \times 5 =$ 8 7 4 5 6 0 9

5. $49 \div 7 \times 3 - 12 =$ 2 4 3 1 5 9 7

4. $12 \times 4 \div 3 + 30 =$ 9 2 3 0 4 6 8

6. $100 \div 5 \times 3 - 6 =$ 0 1 8 5 4 6 3

Shade by numbers

44

Shade in all the shapes that have numbers you can divide by five to see what's fluttering by.

Deadly six

In this pencil-and-paper game for two, you lose
if you make a line of three that adds up to six.

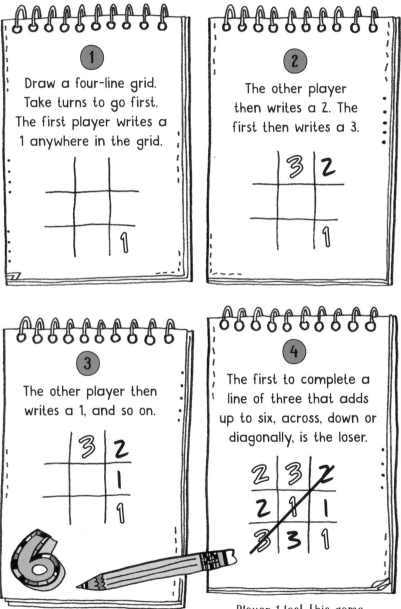

1

Draw a four-line grid.
Take turns to go first.
The first player writes a
1 anywhere in the grid.

2

The other player
then writes a 2. The
first then writes a 3.

3

The other player then
writes a 1, and so on.

4

The first to complete a
line of three that adds
up to six, across, down or
diagonally, is the loser.

Player 1 lost this game.

Mysterious masks

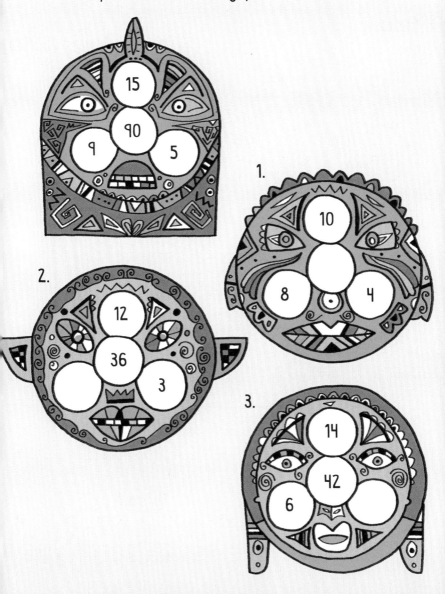

Find out how to use the numbers on the outer circles of the top mask to make the number in the middle using a mixture of adding, subtracting, multiplying or dividing. Then use the same pattern to fill in the gaps on the other masks.

15
90
9   5

1.
10

8   4

2.
12
36

3

3.
14
42
6

Island bridges

Draw straight lines to build bridges horizontally and vertically between the islands so that each island's number matches the number of bridges coming from it. There can be no more than two bridges between any two islands, and bridges may not cross each other.

Word sums

In the words below, each letter stands for a different number between 1 and 7. Can you find out the value of each letter, and of the final word?

See = 14

her = 17

as = 3

free = 19

as the = 21

sea = 9

feathers = ?

Bee line

Find a route for the bee along the dotted lines from the yellow to the orange flower, crossing only odd-numbered flowers.

1	45	26	95	34	86	123	75
18	59	67	41	13	108	11	52
71	33	24	97	6	89	127	103
29	80	7	43	72	63	16	71
102	93	112	53	49	5	22	37
51	15	19	128	12	68	99	141
39	74	47	31	87	35	61	30
65	27	98	130	42	111	8	93
83	136	69	73	29	76	55	108
137	73	21	62	107	23	131	117

Windmill sums

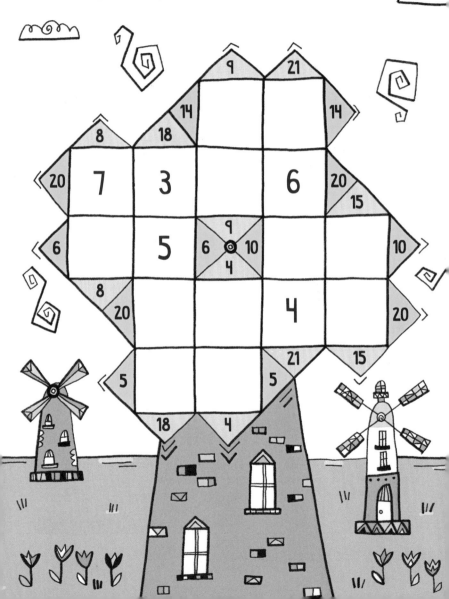

50

Fit numbers from 1 to 9 into the squares so that each line, across and down, adds up to the total shown in the triangles at each end. You can use numbers more than once, but each number in a line must be different.

Balancing act

The first two scales are balanced, but the bottom scales are not. Each robot weighs a different amount. Which one should you add to the right-hand side to make the bottom scales balance? Draw in your answer.

Magic box

Can you fill in the squares with the missing numbers from 1-8, so that every line of three yellow squares adds up to the number in the middle?

	7	
	14	
8	1	

Stone stack

Fill in the blank stones so that each number
is the sum of the two directly beneath it.

Home shopping

Sarah wants to rent an apartment. There are three she likes at the same price, but she needs as much space as possible. Which has the largest area?

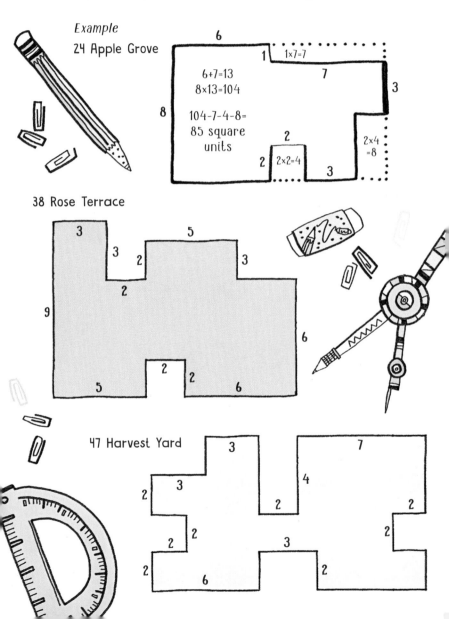

Example
24 Apple Grove

6

1 1×7=7

7

3

6+7=13
8×13=104

104-7-4-8=
85 square
units

8

2

2 2×2=4

2×4
=8

3

38 Rose Terrace

3

3

5

2

3

2

9

6

2

2

5

6

47 Harvest Yard

3

7

3

2

4

2

2

2

2

2

2

3

2

2

6

Last pebble

A game for two. Take turns to cross out as many pebbles from one row as you like. Whoever crosses out the very last pebble loses the game. Take turns going first.

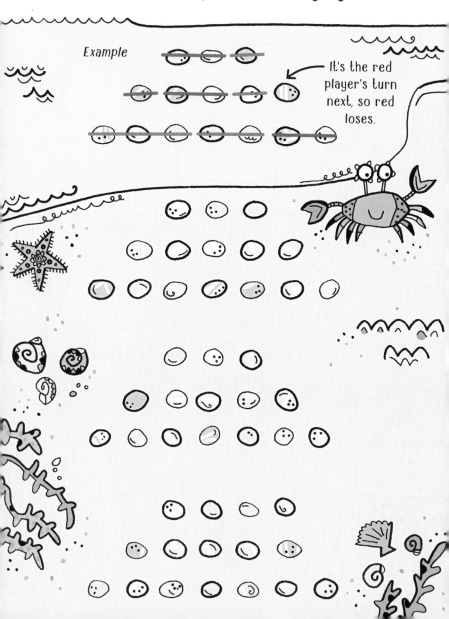

Example

It's the red player's turn next, so red loses.

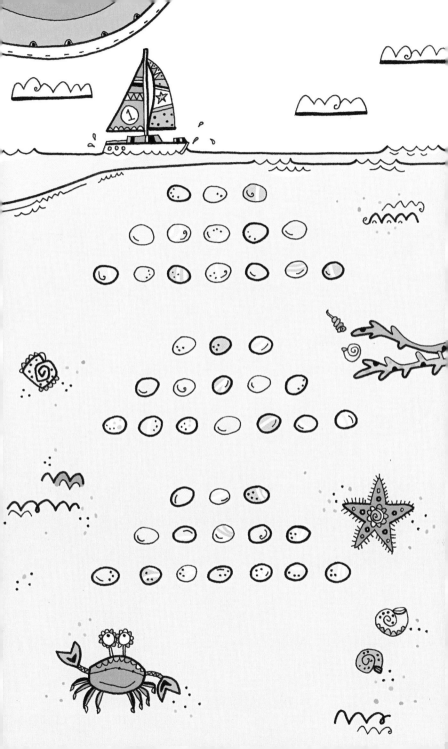

Busy beavers

Benny the beaver can drag twice as much wood as Benji the beaver but Benji can drag it twice as fast.

If Benny can drag six logs in six minutes, how many logs could Benji drag in the same time?

Answer: ....

Missing signs

Add the missing sign $+$ $-$ $\times$ or $\div$
to each calculation to make it correct.

Example:

$$5 + 4 \quad 3 - 2 - 1 = 49 \; \times$$

$$5 + 4 \quad 3 + 2 - 1 = 49 \; \checkmark$$

(5 + 432 - 1 does not equal 49, but 5 + 43 + 2 - 1 does.)

1. $5 \quad 4 - 3 \quad 2 \quad 1 = 23$

2. $5 \quad 4 \quad 3 + 2 + 1 = 21$

3. $5 \times 4 + 3 \quad 2 \quad 1 = 51$

4. $5 - 4 \quad 3 \quad 2 \times 1 = 33$

5. $5 + 4 \quad 3 + 2 \quad 1 = 50$

6. $5 \quad 4 \times 3 \quad 2 + 1 = 161$

Shade by numbers

Shade in all the shapes that have a number you can divide by four to see an early bird.

Confection selection

You have 1.00 to spend on treats.
Which ones should you buy to
spend that exact amount?

Allsorts
0.11

Bonbons
0.19

Bubblegum
0.13

Gummi
bears
0.07

Flying saucers
0.04

Lollipops
0.21

Pear drops
0.09

Jellybeans
0.14

Sugar mice
0.16

Letter numbers

A pen-and-paper game
for two or more players

1

In this game, each letter of
the alphabet is worth points:
a=1, b=2, and so on to z=26.

The longest words
don't always win...

2

One player calls out a
category, such as animals,
sports, jobs or countries.

giraffe = 52

zebra = 52

3

Everybody has a minute to
write down something in that
category. Single words only, so
not "polar bear," for example.

lynx = 75

alligator = 95

4

Now add up your points and
share your sums (you can
use a calculator if you have
one) to see who's won.

chimpanzee = 100

squirrel = 119

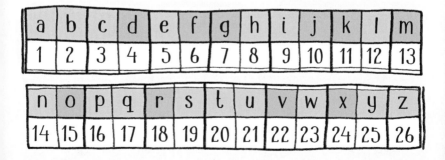

a	b	c	d	e	f	g	h	i	j	k	l	m
1	2	3	4	5	6	7	8	9	10	11	12	13

n	o	p	q	r	s	t	u	v	w	x	y	z
14	15	16	17	18	19	20	21	22	23	24	25	26

Adding animals

The animals in the sum below represent
the numbers 2, 4, 6 and 8. Can you find
out which animal stands for which number?

= .... = ... = 2 = ...

Shield designs

Decorate each soldier's shield differently, according to the
number in the middle. Draw lines starting from that number
on the rim to the next number in its times table, and then
the next one, and so on. When you reach double figures,
just count the last digit, so, for example, 10=0.

Example:

Roman sudoku

✳ The grid below is made up of six blocks, each containing
six squares. Fill in the blank squares so that each block, row
and column contains all the Roman numerals from I to VI.

I = 1   II = 2   III = 3   IV = 4   V = 5   VI = 6

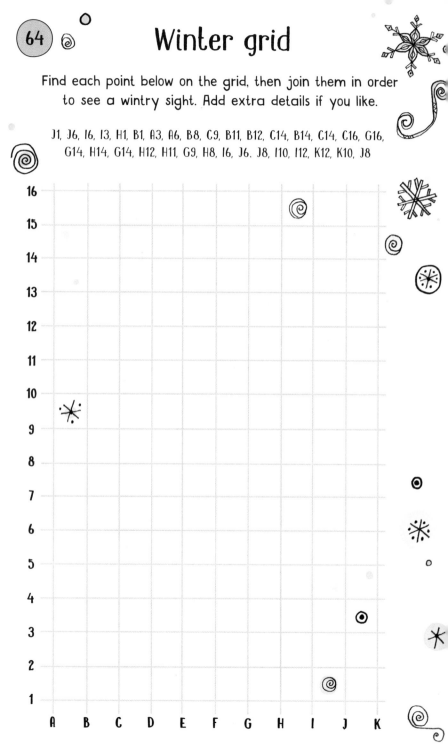

Winter grid

Find each point below on the grid, then join them in order to see a wintry sight. Add extra details if you like.

J1, J6, I6, I3, H1, B1, A3, A6, B8, C9, B11, B12, C14, B14, C14, C16, G16, G14, H14, G14, H12, H11, G9, H8, I6, J6. J8, I10, I12, K12, K10, J8

64

Word sums

In the words below, each letter stands
for a number between 1 and 9. Can
you find out the value of each
letter, and the final word?

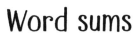

Look	=	17
on	=	5
a	=	3
new	=	16
fall	=	17
of	=	3
snow	=	20

snowflake =

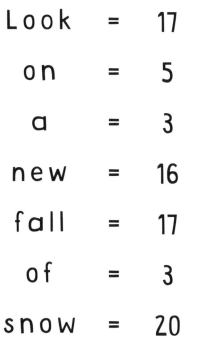

Target number

A pencil-and-paper game for two or more players

1

To prepare this game, take turns to shut your eyes and use a pencil to pick four numbers each, from the opposite page.

Player 1:
3178
Player 2:
7357

2

Next, pick one extra number each and put them together to make one two-digit target number.

26

3

Now you each use some or all of your numbers to create a calculation that makes a number as close to the target number as you can. Give yourselves two minutes.

You can use: (+) (−) (×) (÷)

4

Check and compare your workings to find the winner.

$3 \times 8 + 1 = 25$

$3 \times 7 + 5 = 26$

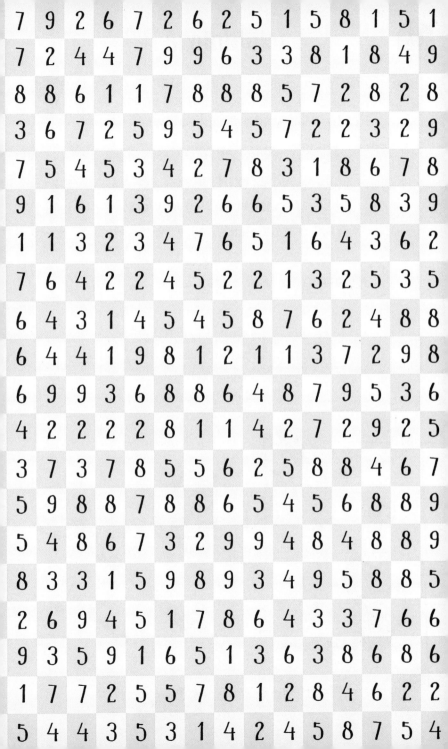

Riddle

As I was going to St. Ives,
I met a man with seven wives.
Every wife had seven sacks,
Every sack had seven cats,
Every cat had seven kittens.
Kittens, cats, sacks, wives,
How many were going to St. Ives?

Read the rhyme carefully.
Can you find out how many
living things were going
to St. Ives?

Bug-eating monsters

Each monster will only eat bugs with numbers that can be divided by the number of eyes it has. Put a star by the monster that eats the most bugs.

26
21
6
18
3
15
4
43
7
20
30
27
32
28
40
23
33
11
5
8
16
44
9
34

Missing shell

Each of the four types of shells below has a different value between one and nine. Figure out the values of the shells, and draw in the missing one. The sum of each row and column is shown.

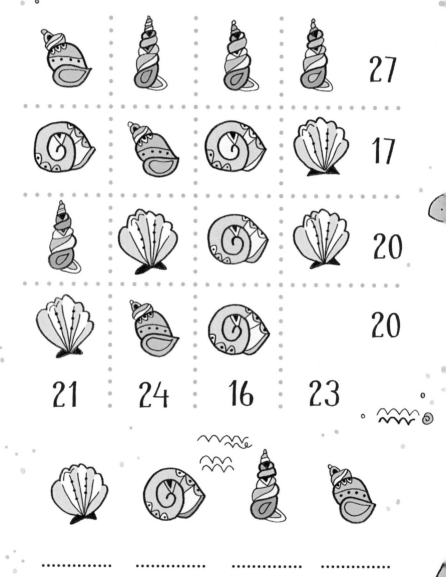

27

17

20

20

21   24   16   23

Starfish sums

Fill in the missing numbers on each starfish so that the
ones on each arm add up to the one in the middle.

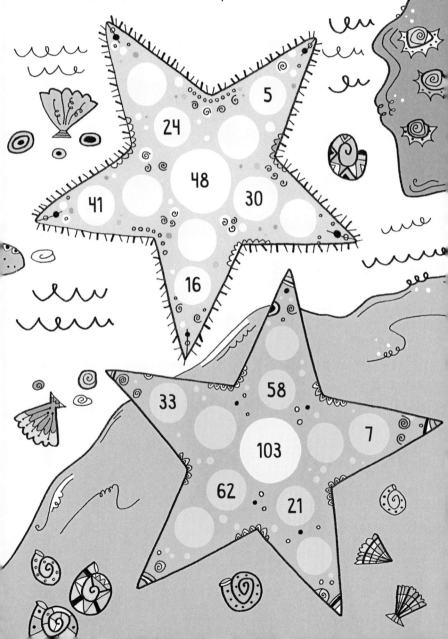

5

24

48

41

30

16

33

58

103

7

62

21

Hands up!

A lively guessing game for three or more players

1

Everyone stands in a circle with their hands behind their backs. On each hand, they stick out five fingers, or none at all.

2

Choose someone to start. She guesses the total number of fingers sticking out.

Twenty!

3

Everyone takes turns to guess. All the guesses must be different.

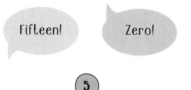

Fifteen!   Zero!

4

On a count of "One, two, three, hands up!" everyone raises their hands to reveal the true total.

5

If anyone guessed right, they choose another player, who can now only play with one hand.

6

The player left of the starting player starts a new round.

7

If you're chosen twice, you're out. The last player still in is the winner.

Tip: Use other players' guesses as clues to the number of fingers they have showing.

Can you fit the missing numbers into the orange cells so that they make an unbroken chain from 1–37?

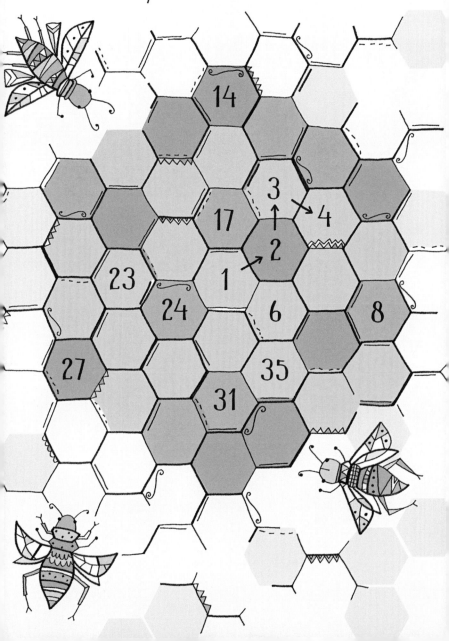

How many rabbits?

Two pairs of rabbits each have eight baby rabbits.
Eight months later, the new rabbits pair up. One month
later, each new pair has eight baby rabbits. How
many rabbits are there now altogether?

Magic squares

Fit the missing numbers from 1-16 into the squares below so that every line of four numbers in every direction adds up to 34.

~~1~~ 2 3 4 5 6 ~~7~~ ~~8~~ ~~9~~ 10 ~~11~~ 12 ~~13~~ 14 ~~15~~ ~~16~~

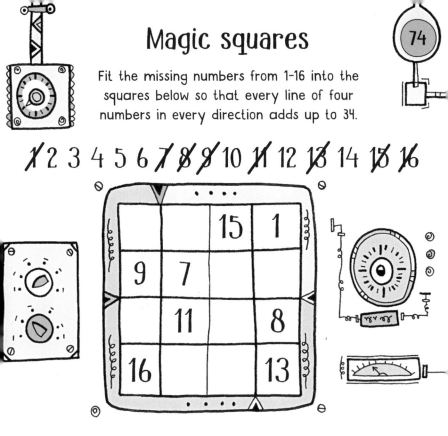

		15	1
9	7		
	11		8
16			13

1 ~~2~~ ~~3~~ ~~4~~ 5 ~~6~~ 7 8 ~~9~~ ~~10~~ 11 12 13 ~~14~~ 15 16

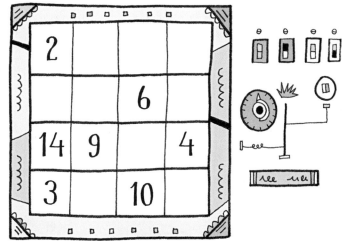

2			
		6	
14	9		4
3		10	

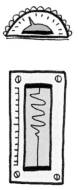

Calculation trail

Can you complete this super-sized calculation, doing each part as you reach it?

Start here

8 **+** 6 **÷** 2

×

5 **÷** 1 **+** 7

−

7 **×** 4 **+** 8

÷

= 3 **−** 5

Ringed planets

Find out the number sequences on the rings and add the missing numbers in the blue circles.

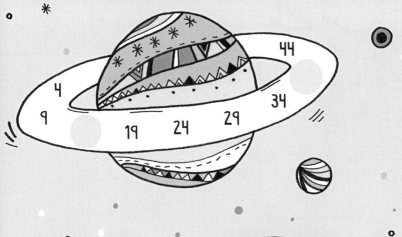

44

4

9

34

19   24   29

8

18

60

27

57

42   53

0

1

1

2

5   8   13

Skip counting

A game for two or more players

1

Skip counting is when you don't count in 1s, but use another number. For example, skip counting in 2s: 2, 4, 6, 8, 10...

2

In this game, someone chooses a number between two and nine, and you all skip count with it.

Example (3s):

3   6   9   12   15   18

3

Sit facing each other. Agree on a target number, such as 50, and see if you can skip count together until you reach or pass it. If someone makes a mistake, start again.

4

If you're all finding this too easy, try starting from different numbers:

Example (skip counting in 3s, starting from 5):

5   8   11   14   17   20

Magic kite

Can you fill in the diamonds with the missing numbers
from 1-8, so that every line of three red diamonds
adds up to the number in the middle?

5

15

8

1

Greater, lesser, equals

Add the signs > (greater than)
< (less than) or = (equals)
to make the statements true.

Example:

| The number of little pigs in the story | **=** | The number of blind mice in the rhyme |

| The number of hours on a clock face | | The number of fingers on your hands |

| The number of vowels in English | | The number of days in a week |

| The number of main compass directions | | The number of suits in a deck of cards |

| The number of legs on a spider | | The number of sides on a hexagon |

| The number of months in a year | | The number of signs of the Zodiac |

| The number of years in a decade | | The number of players in a soccer team |

Lily pad loop

80

Join the lily pads horizontally and vertically to make one big loop with no crossed lines or loose ends. A square of lily pads with a number shows how many sides it has in the loop.

Example:

3	2
	2
3	1

1

2   0   3

3

3

Grazing snails

Each leaf's number shows how many minutes and seconds a snail will take to eat it. Which snail will be last to finish eating its trail of leaves?

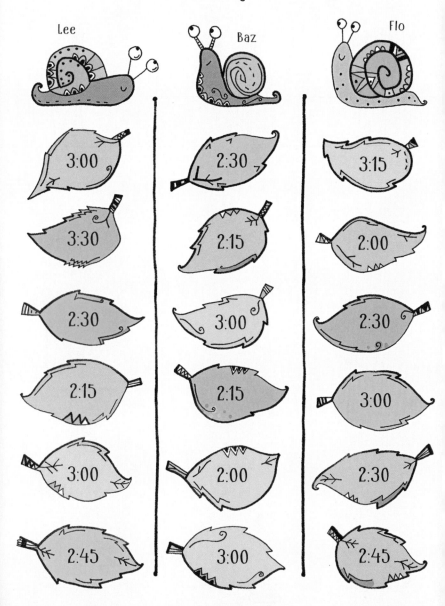

Lee

| 3:00 |
| 3:30 |
| 2:30 |
| 2:15 |
| 3:00 |
| 2:45 |

Baz

| 2:30 |
| 2:15 |
| 3:00 |
| 2:15 |
| 2:00 |
| 3:00 |

Flo

| 3:15 |
| 2:00 |
| 2:30 |
| 3:00 |
| 2:30 |
| 2:45 |

Six sudoku

The grid below is made up of six blocks, each containing six squares. Fill in the blank squares so that each block, row and column contains all the numbers 1 to 6.

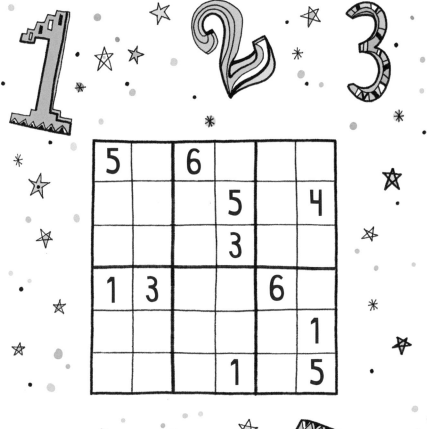

Brain twister

Call out how many words there are on each hut as fast as you can without making any mistakes. It's trickier than it seems.

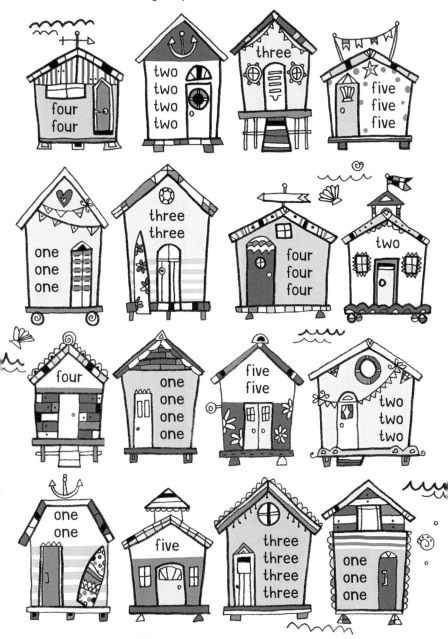

Solution search

Solve the calculations, then draw around
the answers hidden in the numbers.

Example: $6 × 5 ÷ 2 - 3 =$ 1 5 6 (12) 4 7

1. $8 × 4 ÷ 2 - 1 =$ 4 3 15 8 7 6

2. $54 ÷ 6 × 4 - 6 =$ 9 2 5 7 3 0 2

3. $11 × 3 + 9 - 4 =$ 3 8 6 12 5 4

4. $8 × 6 ÷ 12 × 2 =$ 4 6 8 5 0 3 1

5. $16 ÷ 8 × 5 × 13 =$ 2 1 3 0 6 9 5

6. $96 ÷ 3 × 2 + 7 =$ 6 2 4 5 8 7 1

Best bus

Lily is in Upper Tingle, and wants to visit her friend Ed in Snood. The buses stop for two minutes at every town marked in red, but stop for ten in Tingleton. Each road has a travel time, too. Which bus will get Lily there earliest, and when will she arrive?

Key: 9:00 bus ▬▬▬
9:30 bus ▬▬▬

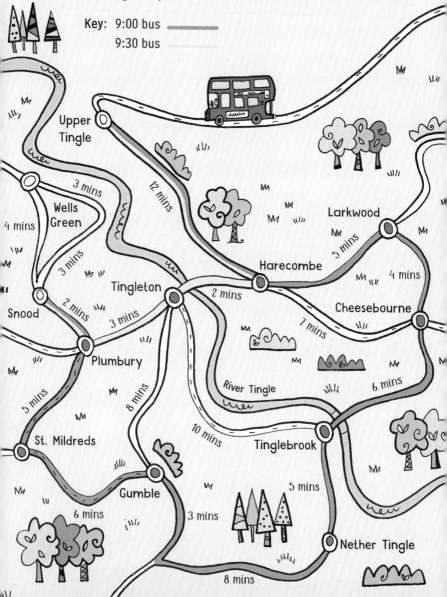

Upper Tingle

3 mins

12 mins

Wells Green

4 mins

3 mins

Larkwood

5 mins

Harecombe

4 mins

2 mins

Tingleton

2 mins

3 mins

Cheesebourne

Snood

7 mins

Plumbury

River Tingle

6 mins

5 mins

8 mins

St. Mildreds

10 mins

Tinglebrook

5 mins

Gumble

3 mins

6 mins

Nether Tingle

8 mins

Woodland puzzle

Each of the four woodland things below has a
different value between one and nine. Figure out
the value of each thing, and draw in the missing
one. The sum of each line and column is shown.

Animal weigh-in

The first three scales are balanced, but the bottom scales are not. Draw in the missing animal on the left-hand side to make the bottom scales balance.

Magic star

Finish filling in all the numbers from 1-12 so
that each line of four numbers adds up to 26.

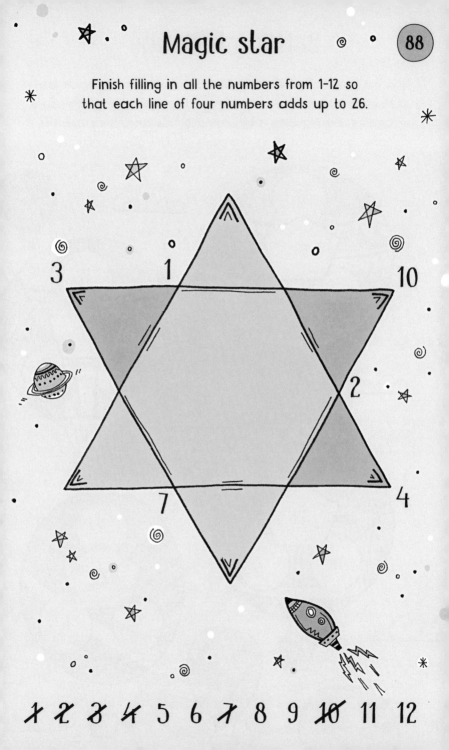

3   1   10

2

7   4

1̶ 2̶ 3̶ 4̶ 5 6 7̶ 8 9 1̶0̶ 11 12

Baffling balloons

Find out how to use the numbers on the outer circles of the top balloon to make the number in the middle using a mixture of adding, subtracting, multiplying or dividing. Then use the same pattern to fill in the gaps on the other balloons.

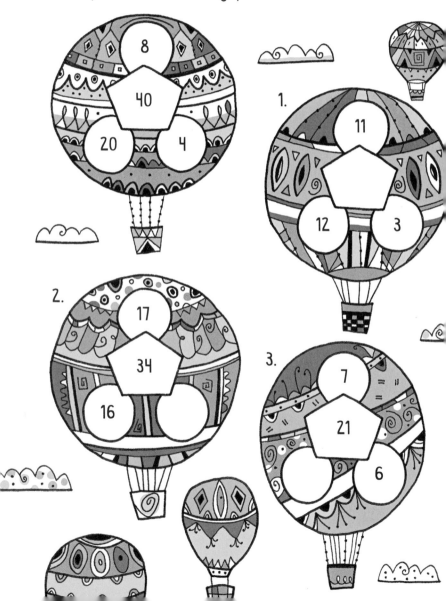

8

40

20   4

1.

11

12   3

2.

17

34

16

3.

7

21

6

Boxed in

90

A game for two players

1

Start by drawing a box. The starting player chooses a number from 1-30, and writes it in the box. The other player writes a different number.

2

The starting player now subtracts the smaller number from the larger one, and writes the answer in the box.

3

Now take turns to make new numbers by subtracting numbers in the box from each other.

4

The first player that can't make a new number loses. Take turns to start.

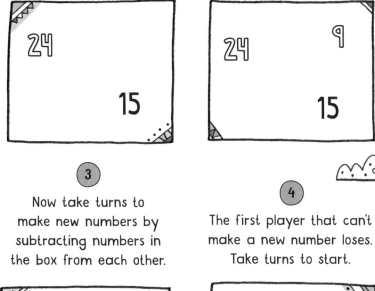

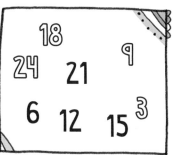

The 2nd player lost this game.

Darts dilemma

You are playing darts. You throw three darts,
which all hit the board in different places.

1. What is the highest score you could make?
2. What is the highest score you could
   make hitting only orange sections?
3. What is the highest score you could
   make hitting only green sections?

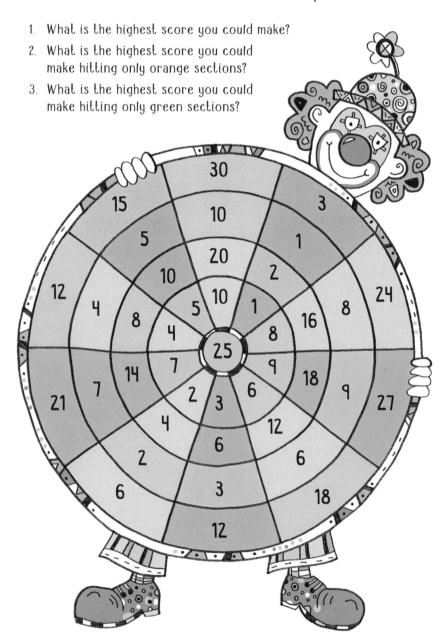

Calculation trail

Can you complete this super-sized calculation,
doing each part as you reach it?

50 — 26 x 3

Start here

3 ÷ 9 + 6

x

6 − 6 ÷ 4 +

= 5 x 3

Number criss-cross

Can you fit all the numbers into the spaces?

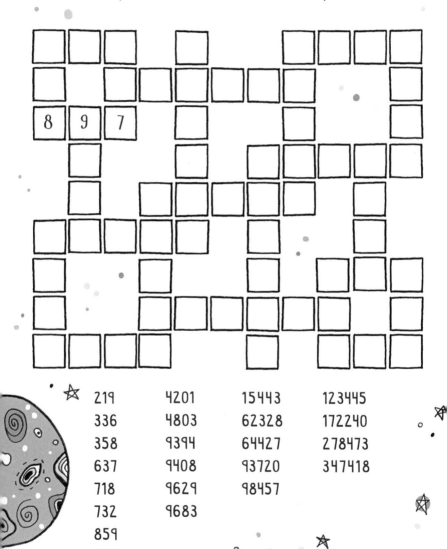

8 9 7

219	4201	15443	123445
336	4803	62328	172240
358	9394	64427	278473
637	9408	93720	347418
718	9629	98457	
732	9683		
859			
~~897~~			

Moon hopper

The spaceship crew need to reach Planet Kodo, hopping between its many moons on the way. They need 100 more fuel units exactly to reach Kodo. They can stop at white moons with odd numbers, pink moons with even numbers, or any blue moon. Plot their route.

Kodo

Pumpkin patches

Draw lines to fence off the field into six pumpkin patches so that each patch has the same number of squares as pumpkins.

100 deer

Between them, four rangers look after 100 deer.
Figure out how many belong to each one.

Ranger Mike has ten more
deer than Ranger Laura.

Ranger Carly has twenty
fewer deer than Ranger Claire.

Ranger Laura has three-quarters the
number of deer that Ranger Carly has.

Mike Laura Carly Claire

15

Flower gardens

Can you draw one straight fence along a dotted line to divide the area into two gardens with the same number of flowers?

Shade by numbers

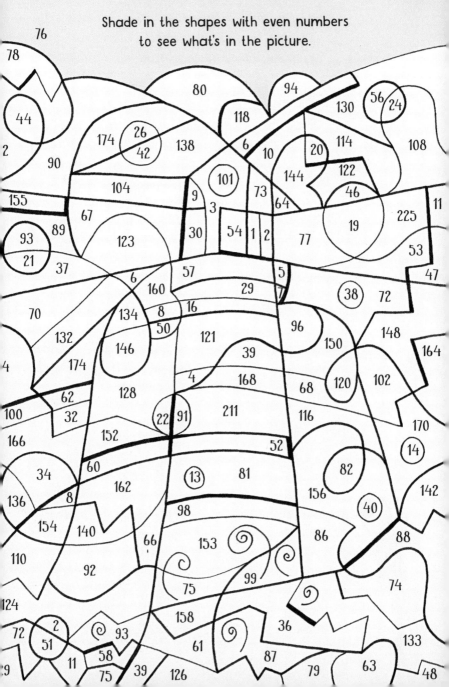

Shade in the shapes with even numbers
to see what's in the picture.

Greater, lesser, equals

Add the signs > (greater than)
< (less than) or = (equals)
to make the statements true.

Example:

| The number of bears that Goldilocks met | **=** | The number of Ugly Sisters Cinderella had |

The number of years of bad luck breaking a mirror is said to bring

The number of lives cats are said to have

The number of faces on a cube

The number of legs on a beetle

The number of singers in a duet

The number of moons orbiting the Earth

The number of days in three weeks

The number of spots on a dice

The number of sides on a rectangle

The number of toes on a foot

The number of legs on an octopus

The number of strings on a standard guitar

Mounting up

Fill the snowcaps so that each number
is the sum of the two directly beneath it.

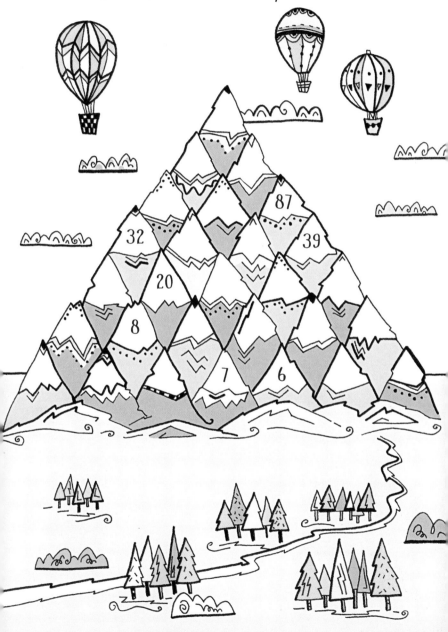

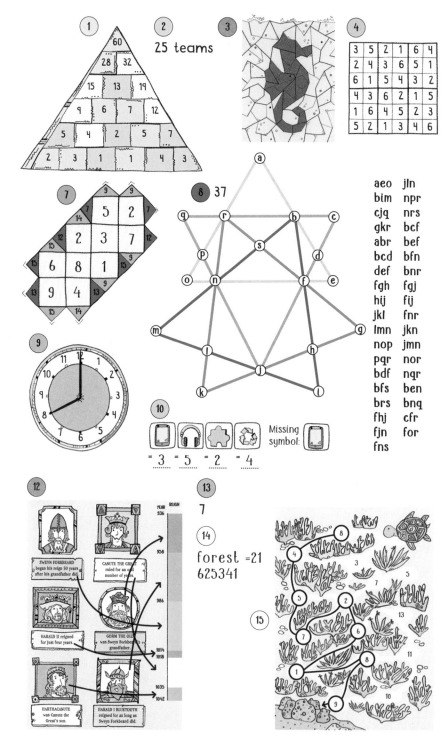

1

60
28 | 32
15 | 13 | 19
9 | 6 | 7 | 12
5 | 4 | 2 | 5 | 7
2 | 3 | 1 | 1 | 4 | 3

2 25 teams

3

4

3	5	2	1	6	4
2	4	3	6	5	1
6	1	5	4	3	2
4	3	6	2	1	5
1	6	4	5	2	3
5	2	1	3	4	6

7

9 | 9
7 | 5 | 2 | 7
14 | | |
12 | 2 | 3 | 7 | 12
15 | 6 | 8 | 1 | 15
15 | 9 | 4 | 9
13 | | 13
15 | 14

8 37

aeo jln
bim npr
cjq nrs
gkr bcf
abr bef
bcd bfn
def bnr
fgh fgj
hij fij
jkl fnr
lmn jkn
nop jmn
pqr nor
bdf nqr
bfs ben
brs bnq
fhj cfr
fjn for
fns

9

10
= 3 = 5 = 2 = 4
Missing symbol:

12

YEAR | REIGN

536

SWEYN FORKBEARD began his reign 50 years after his grandfather did.

958

CANUTE THE GREAT ruled for an odd number of years.

986

HARALD II reigned for just four years.

GORM THE OLD was Sweyn Forkbeard's grandfather.

1014
1018

1035

HARTHACANUTE was Canute the Great's son.

HARALD I BLUETOOTH reigned for as long as Sweyn Forkbeard did.

1042

13
7

14
forest = 21
625341

15

16

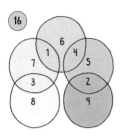

17

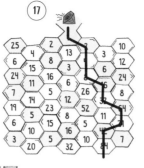

18

2	3	4	5	6	7
3	4	5	6	7	8
4	5	6	7	8	9
5	6	7	8	9	10
6	7	8	9	10	11
7	8	9	10	11	12

1. 7
2. 2 and 12
3. b

19

20

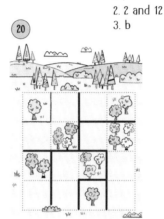

21

No

22

	Army ants	Aztec ants	Bullet ants	Leafcutter ants	Total
Workers	8,000	1,587	185	230	10,002
Soldiers	2,000	405	43	60	2,508
Drones	19	12	15	9	55
Queens	1	1	2	1	5
Total	10,020	2,005	245	300	12,570

24

1.
4
30
2 8

2.
5
29
6 7

3.
9
17
10 3

25

1. 1 2 × 3 + 4 − 5 = 35
2. 1 2 + 3 4 − 5 = 41
3. 1 2 × 3 ÷ 4 + 5 = 14
4. 1 + 2 + 3 + 4 − 5 = 5
5. 1 2 − 3 + 4 5 = 54
6. 1 2 3 + 4 5 = 168

26

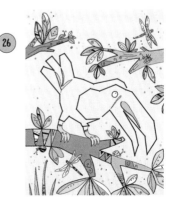

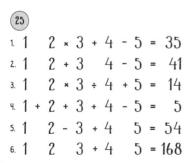

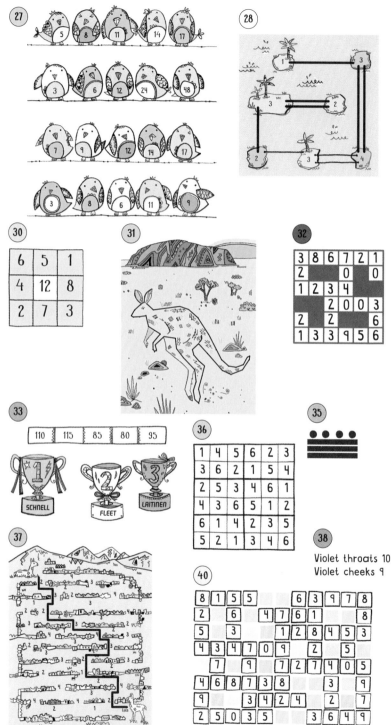

41

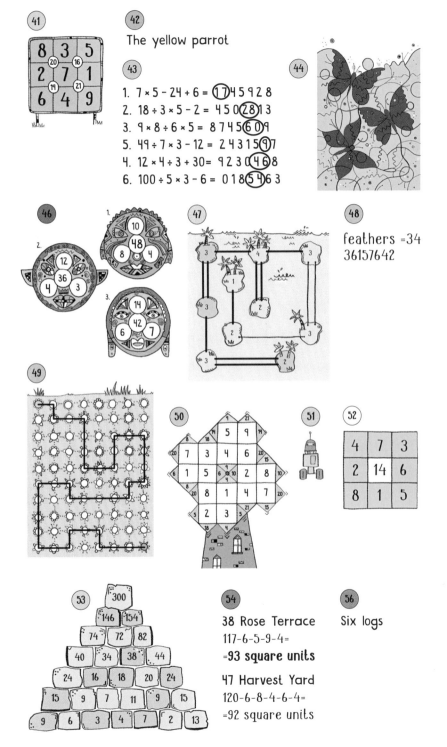

8	3	5
(20)	(16)	
2	7	1
(19)	(21)	
6	4	9

42

The yellow parrot

43

1. $7 \times 5 - 24 + 6 =$ (17) 4 5 9 2 8
2. $18 \div 3 \times 5 - 2 =$ 4 5 0 (28) 1 3
3. $9 \times 8 \div 6 \times 5 =$ 8 7 4 5 (60) 9
5. $49 \div 7 \times 3 - 12 =$ 2 4 3 1 5 (9) 7
4. $12 \times 4 \div 3 + 30 =$ 9 2 3 0 (46) 8
6. $100 \div 5 \times 3 - 6 =$ 0 1 8 (54) 6 3

44

46

1.
- 10
- 48
- 8, 4

2.
- 12
- 36
- 4, 3

3.
- 14
- 42
- 6, 7

47

48

feathers = 34
36157642

49

50

5	9
7	3	4	6
1	5	2	8
8	1	4
2	3

51

52

4	7	3
2	14	6
8	1	5

53

300
146 · 154
74 · 72 · 82
40 · 34 · 38 · 44
24 · 16 · 18 · 20 · 24
15 · 9 · 7 · 11 · 9 · 15
9 · 6 · 3 · 4 · 7 · 2 · 13

54

38 Rose Terrace
$117 - 6 - 5 - 9 - 4 =$
= **93 square units**

47 Harvest Yard
$120 - 6 - 8 - 4 - 6 - 4 =$
= 92 square units

56

Six logs

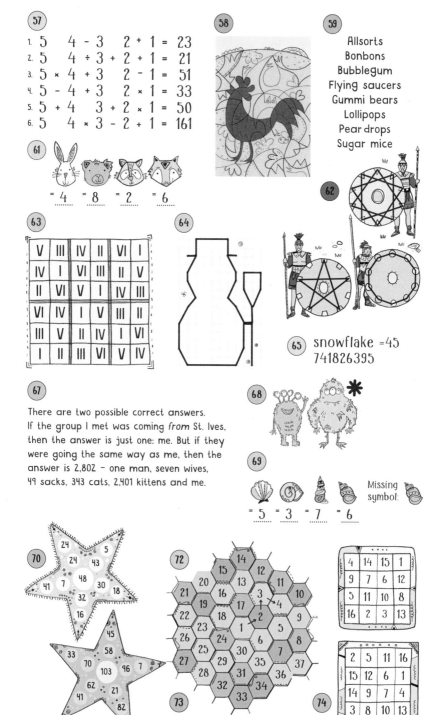

57

1. $5 \quad 4 - 3 \quad 2 + 1 = 23$
2. $5 \quad 4 \div 3 + 2 + 1 = 21$
3. $5 \times 4 + 3 \quad 2 - 1 = 51$
4. $5 - 4 + 3 \quad 2 \times 1 = 33$
5. $5 + 4 \quad 3 + 2 \times 1 = 50$
6. $5 \quad 4 \times 3 - 2 + 1 = 161$

58

59

Allsorts
Bonbons
Bubblegum
Flying saucers
Gummi bears
Lollipops
Pear drops
Sugar mice

61

= 4   = 8   = 2   = 6

62

63

V	III	IV	II	VI	I
IV	I	VI	III	II	V
II	VI	V	I	IV	III
VI	IV	I	V	III	II
III	V	II	IV	I	VI
I	II	III	VI	V	IV

64

65 snowflake = 45
741826395

67

There are two possible correct answers.
If the group I met was coming *from* St. Ives,
then the answer is just one: me. But if they
were going the same way as me, then the
answer is 2,802 – one man, seven wives,
49 sacks, 343 cats, 2,401 kittens and me.

68

69

Missing symbol:

= 5   = 3   = 7   = 6

70

24 5
24 43
41 7 48 30 18
32
16

45
33 58
70 103 96 7
62 21
41 82

72

14
15 12
20 13 11
21 16 3 10
22 19 17 4 9
23 18 1 2
26 24 6 8
27 25 30 35 7
29 31 36 37
28 32 34 33
33

73 84 rabbits

4	14	15	1
9	7	6	12
5	11	10	8
16	2	3	13

74

2	5	11	16
15	12	6	1
14	9	7	4
3	8	10	13

75 1

76

Planet 1 (Saturn-like):
44, 39, 34, 29, 24, 19, 14, 9, 4

Planet 2:
8, 18, 27, 35, 42, 48, 53, 57, 60

Planet 3:
0, 1, 1, 2, 3, 5, 8, 13, 21

78

3, 5, 4, 7, 15, 8, 2, 1, 6

79

Hours on a clock face	>	Fingers on your hands
Vowels in English	<	Days in a week
Main compass directions	=	Suits in a deck of cards
Legs on a spider	>	Sides on a hexagon
Months in a year	=	Signs of the Zodiac
Years in a decade	<	Players in a soccer team

80

2 0
      1
         3
      3
   3

81 Lee 17
Baz 15
Flo 16

82

5	4	6	2	1	3
3	6	1	5	2	4
2	1	4	3	5	6
1	3	5	4	6	2
4	5	2	6	3	1
6	2	3	1	4	5

84

1. $8 \times 4 \div 2 - 1 =$ 4 3 (15) 8 7 6
2. $54 \div 6 \times 4 - 6 =$ 9 2 5 7 (30) 2
3. $11 \times 3 + 9 - 4 =$ 3 (38) 6 1 2 5 4
4. $8 \times 6 \div 12 \times 2 =$ 4 6 (8) 5 0 3 1
5. $16 \div 8 \times 5 \times 13 =$ 2 (130) 6 9 5
6. $96 \div 3 \times 2 + 7 =$ 6 2 4 5 8 (71)

85

9.00 bus ===== =1 hour 12 mins, arrive 10:12
9.30 bus ===== =33 mins, arrive 10:03

86

= 2   = 8   = 6   = 4

Missing symbol: (leaf)

87 (giraffe)

88

8, 3, 1, 12, 10, 11, 2, 6, 7, 9, 4, 5

89

1. 11, 44, 12, 3
2. 17, 34, 16, 8
3. 7, 21, 18, 6

91

1. 82 (30, 27, 25)
2. 73 (27, 25, 21)
3. 74 (30, 24, 20)

92

60

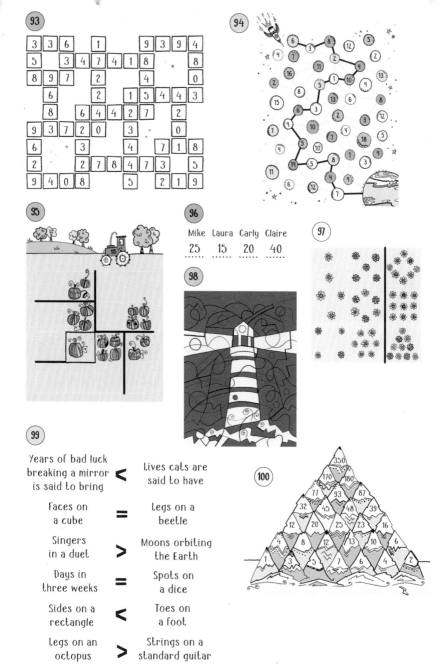